The Three Little Pigs

Once upon a time a lived very happily with her three little . She took good care of them while they were small, but one day she called them to her and said, "Little , you are growing up. It is time for you to go out into the world and

seek your fortunes. Be very
careful, my dears, and watch
out for the bad old  ."

The packed their belongings in whatever they could find to hold them. Then they said a sad goodbye to their and set out to seek their fortunes. They walked together as far as the cross-roads and then each little went his own way. The first little turned to the

right. The second little  turned to the left. The third little  went straight ahead.

The first  had not

gone far when he met a

with a bundle of .

"Please, ," said the ,

"will you give me some of

your so that I may

build a ?"

The kind gave him the

and the built

a and moved in.

Soon the bad old came

down the  and saw the fat 🐷 sitting at the 🪟 of his 🏚️ of 🌾.

"Please, 🐷," called the 🐺, "let me come in."

"No," answered the 🐷.

"Not by the hair of my chinny chin chin."

"Then I'll huff and I'll puff and I'll blow your

 in," said the .

So the  huffed and he puffed and he blew down the  of  and was

going to eat the ,
but the ran away
and hid in the woods.

The second met a
with a bundle of .

"Please, ," he said, "will
you give me some so
that I may build a ?"

The kind gave him the
, and the built

a  . Very soon along came the  and knocked at the  .

"  , let me come in."

"No," said the . "Not by the hair of my chinny chin chin. I will not let you in."

"I'll huff and I'll puff and I'll blow the 🏠 in."

The 🐺 huffed and he puffed and he blew down the 🏠 of 🪵. The 🐷 ran out of the back 🚪 and hid in the woods.

The third 🐷 met a 👨‍🌾

with a load of  .

"Please will you give me

those  to build a  ?"

The  gave him the and the built a . Along came the and saw the little sitting at the of his of " may I come in?"

"Not by the hair of my chinny chin chin."

"I'll huff and I'll puff and I'll blow your in."

The huffed and puffed,

but he could not blow down the  ; so he said, ", I know where there are some  in Mr. Smith's garden. Be ready tomorrow at six o'clock, and we'll get some."

Next morning the little  got up at five o'clock, got the  and was back at home before the  got there.

The  hid his anger and
said, "  , there is a
of juicy red  in Mr.
Brown's orchard. I'll go with

you tomorrow at five o'clock to get some."

The got up at four o'clock, went to the orchard, and was in a picking when he saw the .

"How are the ?" called sly old .

"Fine," answered the .

"I'll throw one down to you."

He threw the so far that,

while the was getting it, the clever ran home.

The would not give up and said, "Let's go to the fair at Shanklin this afternoon."

The little went to the fair ahead of time, bought a butter churn and was on the way home when he saw the at the foot of the hill. Quickly he crawled in-

side the , which overturned
and rolled down the hill. The
 saw the  coming at him,
and he ran away in fright.

The little got home safely and was glad to see the other coming toward his , safe and sound.

The was very angry when he learned what had happened. He climbed right up on the of the little pig's . He planned to go down the and eat up the .

The wise little guessed

what the  was going to do.

He built a blazing fire in the fireplace and filled a big  with water.

When the  came down the 🧱, the little 🐷 took the cover off the 🫕.

The 🐺 fell into the hot